Violin Exam Pieces

ABRSM Grade 5

Selected from the 2016–2019 syllabus

Name

Date of exam

Contents

page

Violin consultant: Philippa Bunting
Footnotes: Terence Charlston (TC), Richard Jones (RJ), Edward Huws Jones (EHJ) and Anthony Burton

Other pieces for Grade 5

LIST A

4 **Mozart** Minuet (*omitting DC*). No. 5 from *Classical and Romantic Pieces*, Book 3, arr. Forbes (OUP)

5 **Telemann** Allegro: 2nd movt from Sonata in G, TWV 41:G1. No. 4 from Telemann, *Six Sonatas for Violin* (Schott)

6 **Vivaldi** Allegro: 1st movt from Concerto in G, Op. 3 No. 3, RV 310 (*violin to play in tuttis*) (Bärenreiter)

LIST B

4 **Carse** Rigaudon. *Classic Carse*, Book 2 (Stainer & Bell)

5 **Liszt** No. 1 *and* No. 2: from Two Waltzes (Hardie Press)

6 **Peguri** An Evening of Romance (*violin melody*). *The French Fiddler*, arr. Huws Jones (Boosey & Hawkes)

LIST C

4 **M. Arnold** No. 1 from *Four Scottish Dances*, Op. 59, arr. Gedge (Novello)

5 **Ives** Allegro: 1st movt from Sonata No. 4, 'Children's Day at the Camp Meeting' (*double stops in bb. 48 and 69 optional; ignoring octave ad lib. in bb. 70–7*) (AMP)

6 **Trad. Russian** Two Guitars. *The Gipsy Violin*, arr. Russ-Bovelino (Bosworth)

First published in 2015 by ABRSM (Publishing) Ltd, a wholly owned subsidiary of ABRSM, 24 Portland Place, London W1B 1LU, United Kingdom

Music origination by Andrew Jones
Cover by Kate Benjamin & Andy Potts
Printed in England by Caligraving Ltd, Thetford, Norfolk, on materials from sustainable sources.
Reprinted in 2016.

Andante

Third movement from Sonata in B minor, BWV 1014

Edited by Terence Charlston

J. S. Bach
(1685–1750)

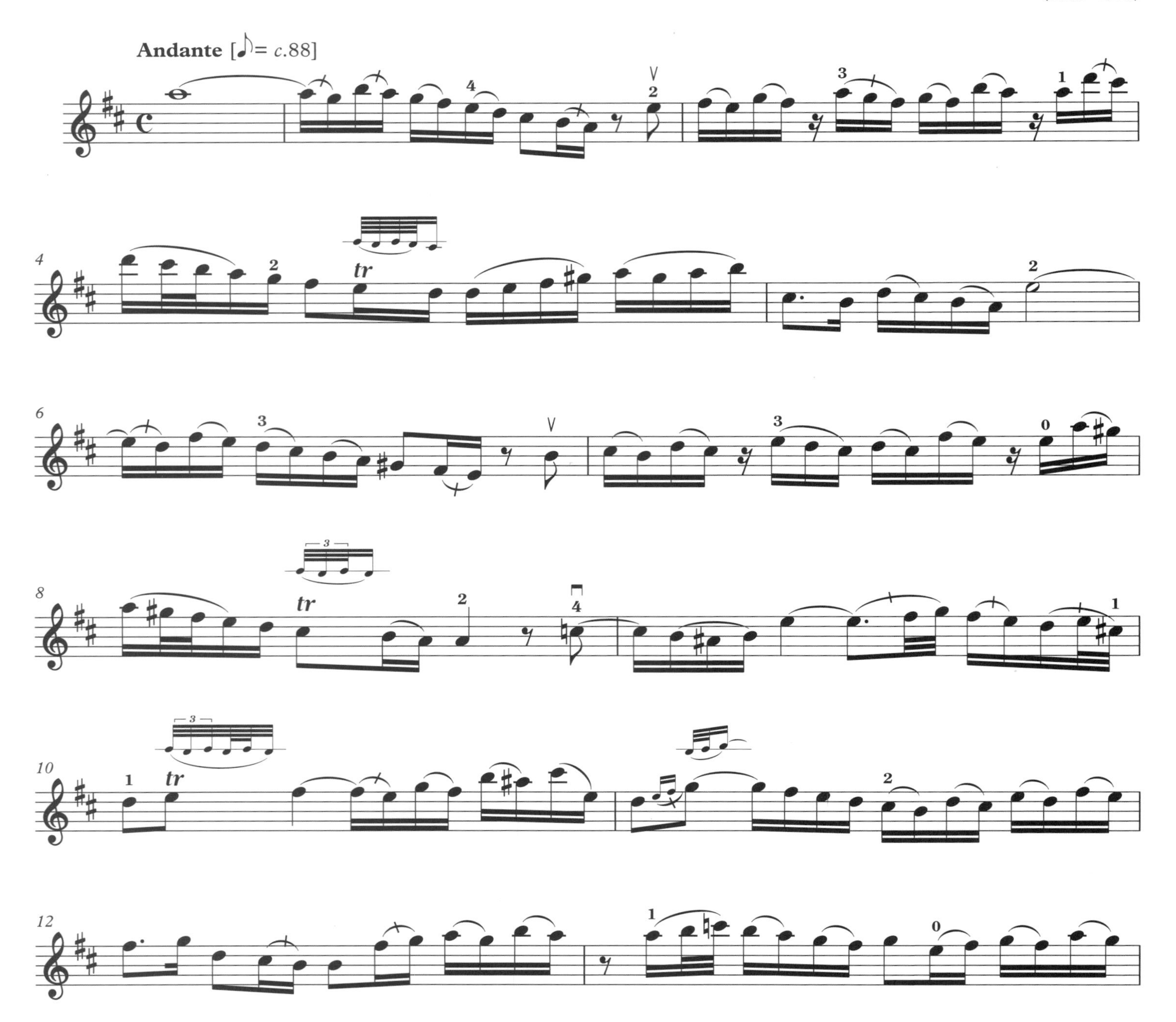

Johann Sebastian Bach (1685–1750) worked as an organist, court musician and church music director in provincial posts in Central Germany. Well known in his own day as a keyboard virtuoso and an authority on the construction of church organs, his genius as a composer was not widely recognized and his fame today rests on the revival of his music which began in the 19th century. Bach's violin and obbligato harpsichord sonatas imitate the texture of a Baroque trio sonata in which the two treble parts (i.e. the violin and the treble keyboard stave) have equal importance, both with each other and with the bass line.

The slurs indicated in the source are often approximately drawn (especially in bb. 4, 8, 14, 18, 21 and 25) and have been unified in parallel passages in this edition. The quaver beams in the left-hand keyboard part are grouped as in the source. Dynamics have been left to the players' discretion. TC

Source: *Manuscript in the hand of Bach's pupil, Johann Christoph Altnickol, Berlin, Staatsbibliothek zu Berlin – Preussischer Kulturbesitz, Musikabteilung, Mus.ms.Bach P 229*

14
16
18
20
22
24
26
28

A:2

Allegro

Fourth movement from Sonata in E, HWV 373

Edited by Richard Jones

attrib. G. F. Handel
(1685–1759)

12 sonatas by (or attributed to) Handel were published by John Walsh of London in 1730–1. This edition was not authorized by the composer, and the title page falsely claimed that the publisher was Jeanne Roger of Amsterdam. Sonatas 10 and 12 from this edition – the latter being the sonata whose finale is selected here – are not known in any other source, and their style seems rather remote from genuine Handel. The deception did not go unnoticed: an inscription in a contemporary hand in the British Library copy reads: 'This is not Mr. Handel's'; and when the 12 sonatas were reissued by Walsh in 1731–2, Nos. 10 and 12 were removed.

Nevertheless, the Sonata in E contains much attractive music in a pseudo-Handelian style. Its four-movement structure (slow–fast–slow–fast) is typical of the *sonata da chiesa* (church sonata). The finale is in a dance-like 3/8 time within an overall binary form. Dynamics have been left to the players' discretion. RJ

Source: *Sonates pour une traversière, un violon ou hautbois con basso continuo* (Amsterdam: J. Roger [correctly, London: John Walsh] 1730–1)

25
30
35
40
[tr]
cresc to end
ignore piano
45
cresc.
49
53
wait for chord
59
63
[tr]

A:3 Ground after the Scotch Humour

from *Other Ayres and Pieces*, 4th Part

Arranged by Edward Huws Jones

Nicola Matteis
(died *c.*1713)

Little is known about the early life of Nicola Matteis, but he was probably born in the mid-17th century in Naples. As a young man he travelled to England (apparently making much of the journey on foot with his precious violin under his coat). Once in London he established himself as the leading virtuoso of his time, reportedly amazing his audiences with the sweetness and brilliance of his playing.

'Ground after the Scotch Humour' calls for a playful and inventive style of performance, with varied dynamics, articulation and phrasing. Quavers are usually short and lively (but not necessarily off the string). Here, as often in Baroque music, the note C on the E string is best played with a fourth finger extension. Matteis indicates numerous 'shakes and trills', which he marks with two parallel lines above the note (//). EHJ

28
34
39
mf
43
47
f
52
56
p
61
mf
66
mp
73
poco rit.
p

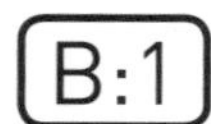

The Holy Boy

A Carol of the Nativity

John Ireland
(1879–1962)

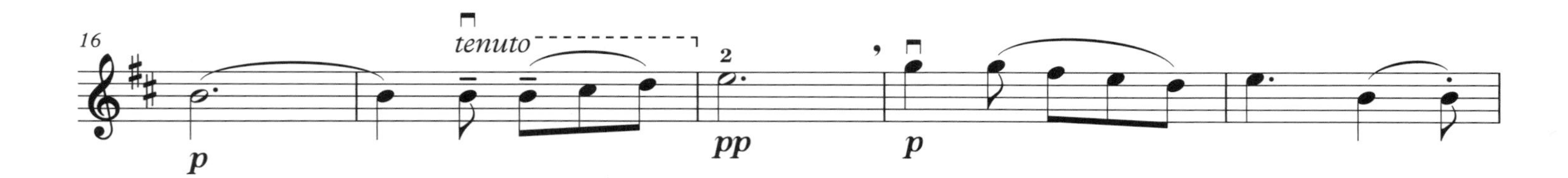

For exam purposes, use of the mute is optional.

John Ireland was born near Manchester, in north-west England, and studied at the Royal College of Music in London, where he later taught. His compositions include orchestral works, chamber music, songs and many pieces for piano. One of the most popular of these is *The Holy Boy*. This was written on Christmas Day 1913, and included in a set of Four Preludes for piano published in 1918. It later appeared in arrangements for various scorings, including versions as a song and a carol for chorus. This arrangement for violin and piano by the composer was published in 1919.

26
pp
cresc. molto

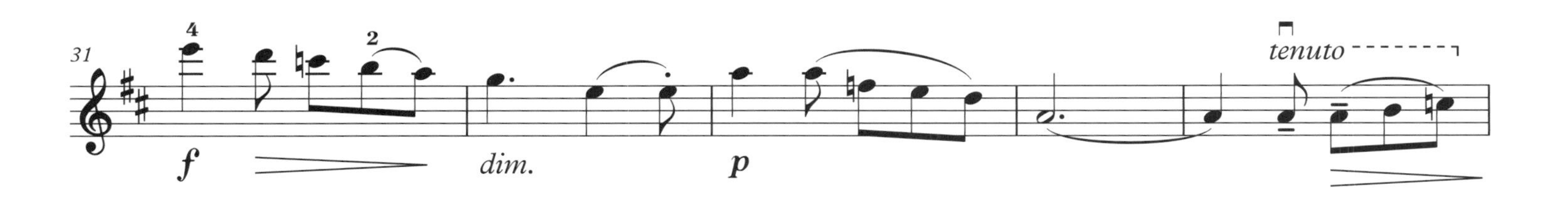
31
tenuto
f
dim.
p

36
pp
ppp

41
pp
p

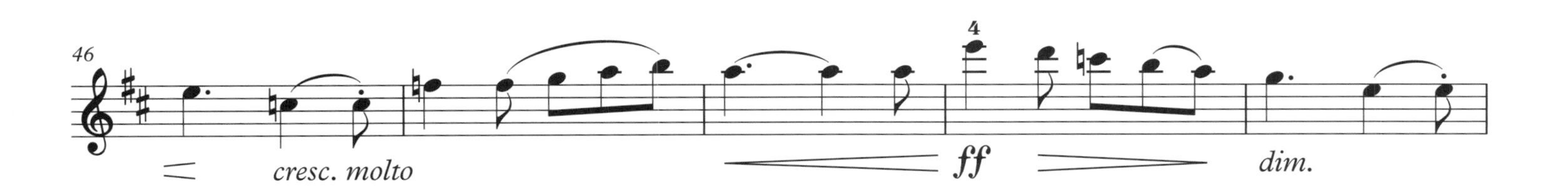
46
cresc. molto
ff
dim.

51
rit.
p dim.
pp

B:2

Rondino

on a Theme of Beethoven

Fritz Kreisler
(1875–1962)

Fritz Kreisler, born in Vienna but later an American citizen, was one of the greatest violinists of his day. He composed and arranged many charming miniatures for the violin, suitable as encores or for 78 rpm records. This Rondino ('little rondo') was dedicated to the Russian American violinist Mischa Elman, and was first recorded by the composer in 1916. The theme is taken from a little-known Rondo in G major for violin and piano (WoO 41) written by Beethoven in 1793/4 and published in 1808. As well as transposing the theme to E flat major, Kreisler transferred it from piano to violin, changed its time signature from 6/8 to 3/4, added *grazioso* to its tempo marking of Allegro, smoothed out its melodic line and gave it a new, flowing accompaniment. He completed the piece (from the end of b. 16) in the musical language of Beethoven's time.

55
62
70
78
III
cantando
86
II
cresc.
con calore
95
semplice
102
109
116
p semplice

Romance

from *The Gadfly*

Arranged by Donald Fraser

Dmitry Shostakovich
(1906–1975)

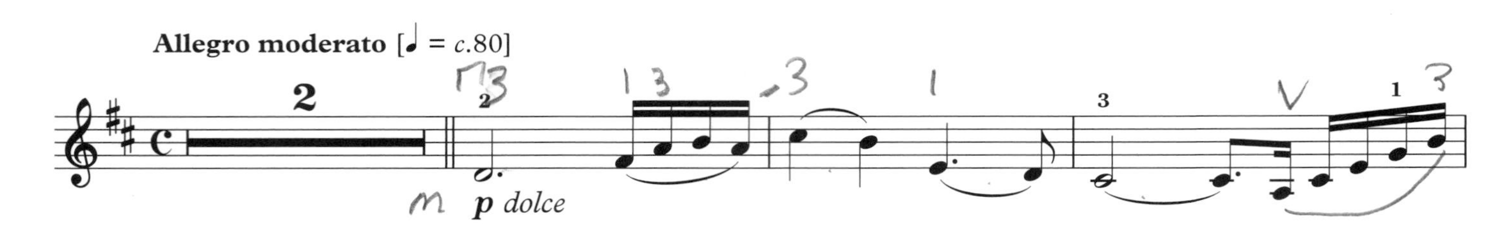

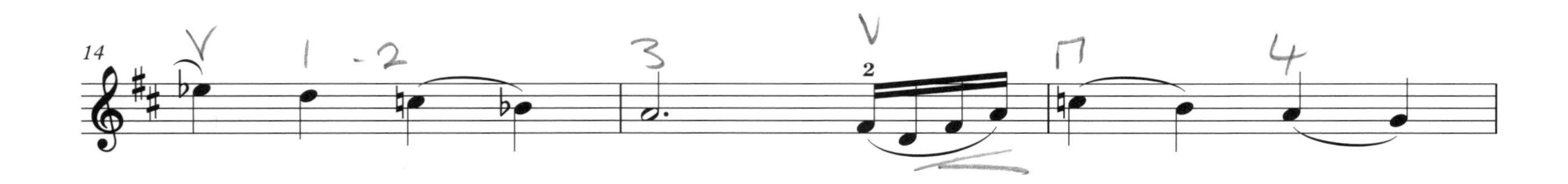

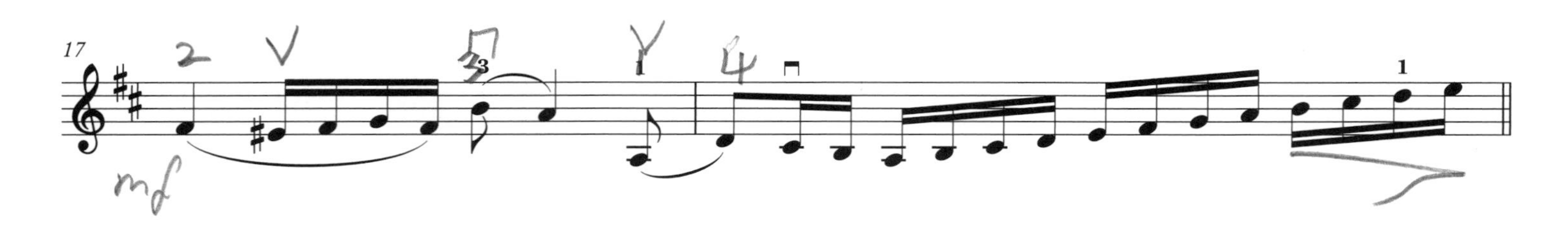

As well as composing operas, symphonies, concertos and other concert works, the Russian composer Dmitri Shostakovich wrote a great deal of film music. *Ovod* (*The Gadfly*), for which he provided the score in 1955, is a romantic drama set in 19th-century Italy. The well-known 'Romance', in the style of an operatic aria of that period, is associated with the hero, a young revolutionary. In Shostakovich's original score, and in the orchestral suite arranged from it by the composer's regular collaborator Lev Atovmyan, the melody is introduced by a solo violin. The arrangement here is by the British-born composer and conductor Donald Fraser.

Violin Exam Pieces

ABRSM Grade 5

Selected from the 2016–2019 syllabus

Piano accompaniment

Contents

page

Violin consultant: Philippa Bunting
Footnotes: Terence Charlston (TC), Richard Jones (RJ), Edward Huws Jones (EHJ) and Anthony Burton

The pieces in this album have been taken from a variety of different sources. Where appropriate, they have been checked with original source material and edited to help the player when preparing for performance. Any editorial additions are given in small print; within square brackets; or, in the case of slurs and ties, in the form ⌒. The fingering and bowing have been amended where necessary to ensure a consistent approach within the album. Details of other editorial amendments or suggestions are given in the footnotes. Fingering, bowing and all editorial additions are for guidance only; they are not comprehensive or obligatory.

ABRSM Violin Exams: requirements

Pieces

In the exam, candidates must play three pieces, one chosen from each of the three syllabus lists (A, B and C). Candidates are free to choose from the pieces printed in this album and/or from the other pieces set for the grade: a full list is given in the violin part with this score as well as in the 2016–2019 Bowed Strings syllabus.

Scales and arpeggios
Sight-reading
Aural tests
} Full details are available online at www.abrsm.org/violin5

First published in 2015 by ABRSM (Publishing) Ltd, a wholly owned subsidiary of ABRSM, 24 Portland Place, London W1B 1LU, United Kingdom

Music origination by Julia Bovee
Cover by Kate Benjamin & Andy Potts
Printed in England by Caligraving Ltd, Thetford, Norfolk

Andante

Third movement from Sonata in B minor, BWV 1014

Edited by Terence Charlston

J. S. Bach
(1685–1750)

Johann Sebastian Bach (1685–1750) worked as an organist, court musician and church music director in provincial posts in Central Germany. Well known in his own day as a keyboard virtuoso and an authority on the construction of church organs, his genius as a composer was not widely recognized and his fame today rests on the revival of his music which began in the 19th century. Bach's violin and obbligato harpsichord sonatas imitate the texture of a Baroque trio sonata in which the two treble parts (i.e. the violin and the treble keyboard stave) have equal importance, both with each other and with the bass line.

The slurs indicated in the source are often approximately drawn (especially in bb. 4, 8, 14, 18, 21 and 25) and have been unified in parallel passages in this edition. The quaver beams in the left-hand keyboard part are grouped as in the source. Dynamics have been left to the players' discretion. TC

Source: *Manuscript in the hand of Bach's pupil, Johann Christoph Altnickol, Berlin, Staatsbibliothek zu Berlin – Preussischer Kulturbesitz, Musikabteilung, Mus.ms.Bach P 229*

tr
[tr]
6
[tr]

tr
tr
tr

Allegro

A:2

Fourth movement from Sonata in E, HWV 373

Edited by Richard Jones

attrib. G. F. Handel
(1685–1759)

12 sonatas by (or attributed to) Handel were published by John Walsh of London in 1730–1. This edition was not authorized by the composer, and the title page falsely claimed that the publisher was Jeanne Roger of Amsterdam. Sonatas 10 and 12 from this edition – the latter being the sonata whose finale is selected here – are not known in any other source, and their style seems rather remote from genuine Handel. The deception did not go unnoticed: an inscription in a contemporary hand in the British Library copy reads: 'This is not Mr. Handel's'; and when the 12 sonatas were reissued by Walsh in 1731–2, Nos. 10 and 12 were removed.

Nevertheless, the Sonata in E contains much attractive music in a pseudo-Handelian style. Its four-movement structure (slow–fast–slow–fast) is typical of the *sonata da chiesa* (church sonata). The finale is in a dance-like 3/8 time within an overall binary form. Dynamics have been left to the players' discretion. RJ

Source: *Sonates pour une traversière, un violon ou hautbois con basso continuo* (Amsterdam: J. Roger [correctly, London: John Walsh] 1730–1)

1.
2.
mf
(mp Zulaikha)
quieter
dim
Cresc to end
mf (Zulaikha)
[tr]

44
50
56
62
[tr]

A:3 Ground after the Scotch Humour

from *Other Ayres and Pieces*, 4th Part

Arranged by Edward Huws Jones

Nicola Matteis
(died *c.*1713)

Little is known about the early life of Nicola Matteis, but he was probably born in the mid-17th century in Naples. As a young man he travelled to England (apparently making much of the journey on foot with his precious violin under his coat). Once in London he established himself as the leading virtuoso of his time, reportedly amazing his audiences with the sweetness and brilliance of his playing.

'Ground after the Scotch Humour' calls for a playful and inventive style of performance, with varied dynamics, articulation and phrasing. Quavers are usually short and lively (but not necessarily off the string). Here, as often in Baroque music, the note C on the E string is best played with a fourth finger extension. Matteis indicates numerous 'shakes and trills', which he marks with two parallel lines above the note (//). EHJ

16
f
f
21
p
26
31

37
mf
43
48
f
53
p
3

57
62
mf
mf
69
mp
mp
75
poco rit.
p
p

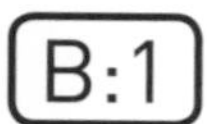

The Holy Boy

A Carol of the Nativity

John Ireland
(1879–1962)

For exam purposes, use of the mute is optional.

John Ireland was born near Manchester, in north-west England, and studied at the Royal College of Music in London, where he later taught. His compositions include orchestral works, chamber music, songs and many pieces for piano. One of the most popular of these is *The Holy Boy*. This was written on Christmas Day 1913, and included in a set of Four Preludes for piano published in 1918. It later appeared in arrangements for various scorings, including versions as a song and a carol for chorus. This arrangement for violin and piano by the composer was published in 1919.

19
p
dim.
p
dim.

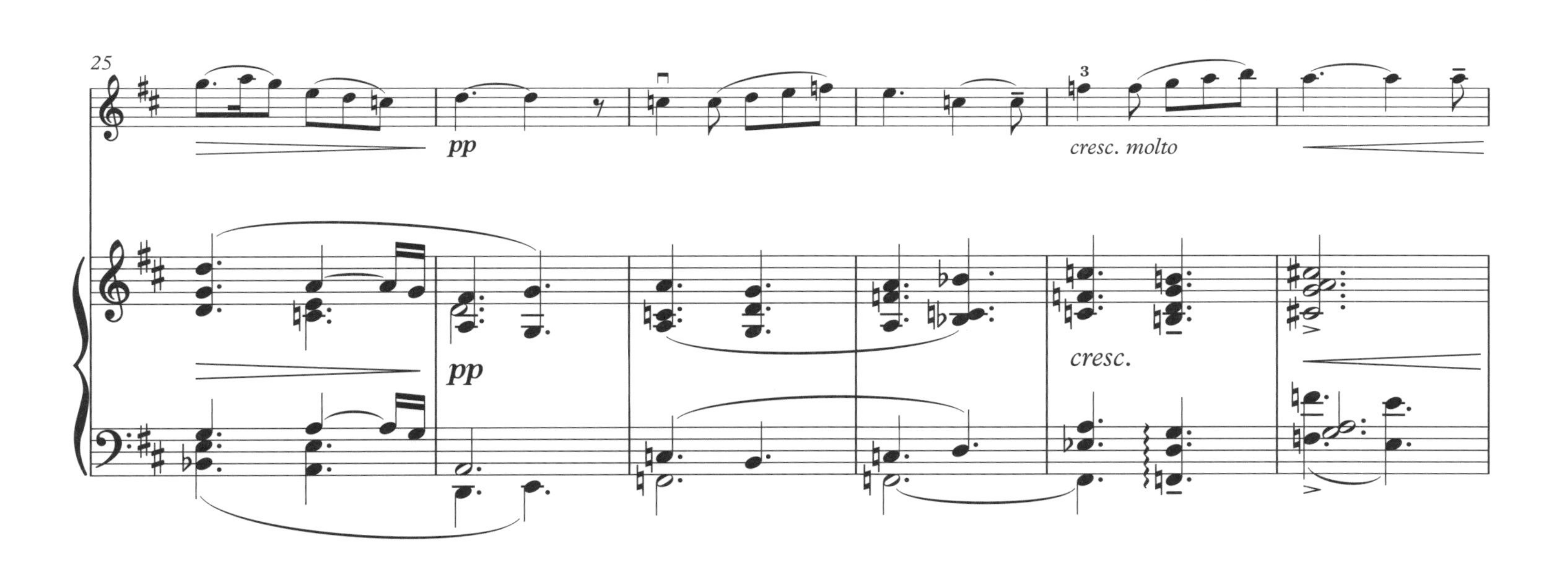
25
pp
cresc. molto
pp
cresc.

31
f
dim.
p
tenuto
pp
mf
dim.
p
pp
ppp

37
ppp
pp
pp
ppp
44
p
cresc. molto
ff
p
cresc.
f
50
rit.
dim.
p dim.
pp
dim.
p dim.
pp
ppp

Rondino

B:2

on a Theme of Beethoven

Fritz Kreisler
(1875–1962)

Fritz Kreisler, born in Vienna but later an American citizen, was one of the greatest violinists of his day. He composed and arranged many charming miniatures for the violin, suitable as encores or for 78 rpm records. This Rondino ('little rondo') was dedicated to the Russian American violinist Mischa Elman, and was first recorded by the composer in 1916. The theme is taken from a little-known Rondo in G major for violin and piano (WoO 41) written by Beethoven in 1793/4 and published in 1808. As well as transposing the theme to E flat major, Kreisler transferred it from piano to violin, changed its time signature from 6/8 to 3/4, added *grazioso* to its tempo marking of Allegro, smoothed out its melodic line and gave it a new, flowing accompaniment. He completed the piece (from the end of b. 16) in the musical language of Beethoven's time.

19
p
cresc.
27
IV
cresc.
cresc.
p
p
34
40
cresc.
cresc.

48
54
60
67
p
f
espress.

75
poco cresc.
82
III
cantando
88
II
cresc.
con calore
94
semplice
p
p

100
105
p
110
cresc.
116
p
p semplice
p

Romance

from *The Gadfly*

Arranged by Donald Fraser

Dmitry Shostakovich
(1906–1975)

As well as composing operas, symphonies, concertos and other concert works, the Russian composer Dmitri Shostakovich wrote a great deal of film music. *Ovod* (*The Gadfly*), for which he provided the score in 1955, is a romantic drama set in 19th-century Italy. The well-known 'Romance', in the style of an operatic aria of that period, is associated with the hero, a young revolutionary. In Shostakovich's original score, and in the orchestral suite arranged from it by the composer's regular collaborator Lev Atovmyan, the melody is introduced by a solo violin. The arrangement here is by the British-born composer and conductor Donald Fraser.

10
a tempo
13
16
19
p dolce

rit.
a tempo
pp
pp
rit.

36
a tempo
p
p
sim.
39
42
rit.
45
a tempo
dim.
dim.
rit.

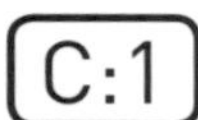

Dream

Gordon Kerry
(born 1961)

Gordon Kerry is an Australian composer, who lives in the rural north-east of the state of Victoria. He has written two operas, and orchestral, chamber and choral music for performers in Australia, Europe and the USA. He composed *Dream* in 1987 for his niece Kerryn, who had recently started learning the violin. The title alludes to 'the dreamtime' of Australian Aboriginal mythology, when the world was created by ancestor spirits, and to the way the piece includes fragmentary, dream-like memories of an Aboriginal melody. Kerry explains that one of his sisters was living on the Noonkanbah Station in the Kimberley region of north-west Australia during the 1970s, when a mining company was given state government permission and police protection to drill for diamonds on a site sacred to the local people. Shortly afterwards, he obtained a recording of a meeting of the local lands council, in which a traditional melody was sung several times. What Kerry calls the 'salient features' of the melody, 'a falling contour over a "gapped" scale', appear in both the violin and piano parts of *Dream*. The *sul tasto* passage should be played over the fingerboard, and *sul pont.* close to the bridge.

nat.
harmonic gliss.
sul IV
repeat presto
repeat presto
mf dim.
mf dim.

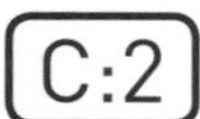

Bathwater Blues

No. 10 from *Creative Variations for Violin*, Vol. 1

Malcolm Miles
(born 1964)

Malcolm Miles studied at Leeds College of Music and the Guildhall School of Music and Drama in London, and is now a performer, on saxophone and flute, and educator in the field of jazz. 'Bathwater Blues' comes from a volume he co-wrote with Jeffery Wilson called *Creative Variations*, designed as a guide to writing or improvising variations on themes or chord-patterns. The piece, Miles says, 'demonstrates different ways of inventing melodies over a 12-bar blues: using triads; using triads with the seventh; using chord shapes and related scales; embellishing chord shapes with chromatic neighbour notes; using the blues scale.'

34
39
44
49

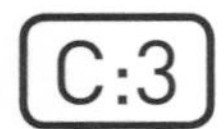

Intermezzo

from *Háry János*

Arranged by Peter Kolman

Zoltán Kodály
(1882–1967)

Zoltán Kodály was one of the leading composers in 20th-century Hungary; much of his music was based on Hungarian folk music (which he and his friend Béla Bartók recorded and transcribed on visits to the countryside), or on old publications of Hungarian dances. Kodály's *Háry János*, first produced in Budapest in 1926, is a play with music, in which a boastful veteran of the Austro-Hungarian army tells and re-enacts the fantastical story of how he single-handedly defeated Napoleon's invading forces and won the heart of a princess. This Intermezzo was written a few weeks before the premiere to cover a change of scenery; it was later included in the popular orchestral suite that Kodály compiled from the score. The piece is based on a *verbunkos*, or 'recruiting dance', taken from a piano tutor published in 1802, István Gáti's *A' Kótábol való klavirozás mestersege*.

11
cresc.
cresc.
15
poco pesante
a tempo
f
f
sf
ff
ff
sf
sf
dim.
dim.
19
mp
mp
poco rinf.
poco rinf. e poco stacc.
23
cresc.
cresc.

27
ff
pesante
a tempo
sff
sff
31
dim.
mp
f
f ben tenuto
35
sf
cresc.
39
ff
4
3
0

p dolce
rit.
a tempo
cresc.
pp
rit.
a tempo
p
rit.
a tempo
dim.
rit.

Dream

Gordon Kerry
(born 1961)

Gordon Kerry is an Australian composer, who lives in the rural north-east of the state of Victoria. He has written two operas, and orchestral, chamber and choral music for performers in Australia, Europe and the USA. He composed *Dream* in 1987 for his niece Kerryn, who had recently started learning the violin. The title alludes to 'the dreamtime' of Australian Aboriginal mythology, when the world was created by ancestor spirits, and to the way the piece includes fragmentary, dream-like memories of an Aboriginal melody. Kerry explains that one of his sisters was living on the Noonkanbah Station in the Kimberley region of north-west Australia during the 1970s, when a mining company was given state government permission and police protection to drill for diamonds on a site sacred to the local people. Shortly afterwards, he obtained a recording of a meeting of the local lands council, in which a traditional melody was sung several times. What Kerry calls the 'salient features' of the melody, 'a falling contour over a "gapped" scale', appear in both the violin and piano parts of *Dream*. The *sul tasto* passage should be played over the fingerboard, and *sul pont.* close to the bridge.

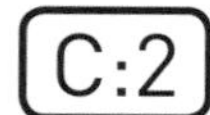

Bathwater Blues

No. 10 from *Creative Variations for Violin*, Vol. 1

Malcolm Miles
(born 1964)

Malcolm Miles studied at Leeds College of Music and the Guildhall School of Music and Drama in London, and is now a performer, on saxophone and flute, and educator in the field of jazz. 'Bathwater Blues' comes from a volume he co-wrote with Jeffery Wilson called *Creative Variations*, designed as a guide to writing or improvising variations on themes or chord-patterns. The piece, Miles says, 'demonstrates different ways of inventing melodies over a 12-bar blues: using triads; using triads with the seventh; using chord shapes and related scales; embellishing chord shapes with chromatic neighbour notes; using the blues scale.'

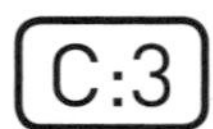

Intermezzo

from *Háry János*

Arranged by Peter Kolman

Zoltán Kodály
(1882–1967)

Zoltán Kodály was one of the leading composers in 20th-century Hungary; much of his music was based on Hungarian folk music (which he and his friend Béla Bartók recorded and transcribed on visits to the countryside), or on old publications of Hungarian dances. Kodály's *Háry János*, first produced in Budapest in 1926, is a play with music, in which a boastful veteran of the Austro-Hungarian army tells and re-enacts the fantastical story of how he single-handedly defeated Napoleon's invading forces and won the heart of a princess. This Intermezzo was written a few weeks before the premiere to cover a change of scenery; it was later included in the popular orchestral suite that Kodály compiled from the score. The piece is based on a *verbunkos*, or 'recruiting dance', taken from a piano tutor published in 1802, István Gáti's *A' Kótábol való klavirozás mestersege*.

poco pesante
a tempo
ff
sf
dim.
mp
poco rinf.
cresc.
ff
pesante
a tempo
ff
sff
dim.
WAIT!
(piano chord)
mp
f
sf
cresc.
ff
ff